¡Gol! ¡Vamos a Jugar!
Goal! Let's Play!

Joe Marriott
Illustrated by Algy Craig Hall

Spanish translation by Marta Belen Saez-Cabero

Mantra Lingua

Me llamo Chen y juego
al fútbol todos los días.

I'm Chen and I play
soccer every day.

Thwack   boing

Goal!

Let's score!

Me llamo Daniella.
Me encanta jugar al
baloncesto con mis
amigos.

My name's Daniella.
I love playing basketball
with my friends.

Boing
phwoop

through the hoop!

Let's shoot!

Me llamo Chet y me encanta jugar al béisbol con mi equipo.

I'm Chet and I love playing baseball with my team.

WHACK

LET'S CATCH!

THUNK  **CAUGHT!**

Me llamo Faris. Papá y yo competimos en una carrera de camellos.

My name's Faris. Daddy and I are racing on a camel.

Humpety!
Bumpety!
Thumpety!

Let's ride!

Me llamo Katy y juego con mi cometa en lo alto de la colina.

I'm Katy and I fly my kite at the top of the hill.

Let's fly!
Whoosh!
zoom!
Zip!

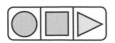

Me llamo Pierre. Soy el corredor más rápido de mi clase.

My name's Pierre. I'm the fastest runner in my class.

Huff puff whiz whistle!

Let's race!

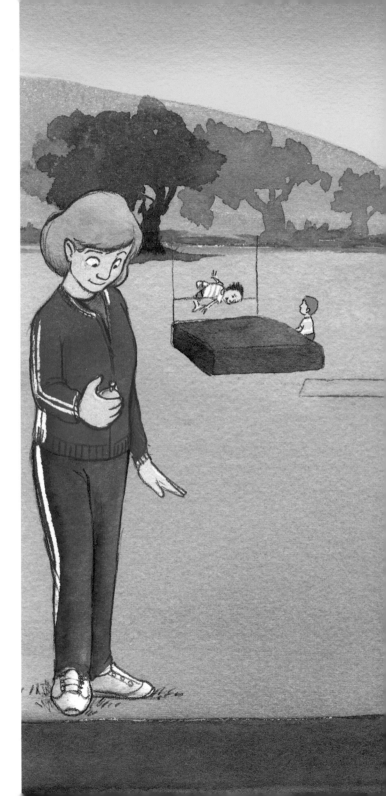

Me llamo Nadia y me encanta nadar con mis amigos en agua fresca.

I'm Nadia and I love swimming with my friends in the cool water.

splish

splash

sploosh!

Let's dive!

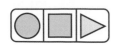

Me llamo James. Juego al tenis con mi familia todos los fines de semana.

My name's James.
I play tennis with my family every weekend.

Whack!

Wham!

Boing!

SLAM!

Let's serve!

Me llamo Marta y estoy aprendiendo yudo en el gimnasio.

I'm Marta and I'm learning judo in the gym.

Spin!

Chop!

Flip!

Flop!

Let's throw!

Me llamo Tomás y puedo
esquiar muy rápido.

I'm Tomas and I can ski
really fast.

Swish! Swerve!
Whiiiiiiiiiiiiiizzzzzzzz z z!

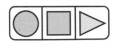

Let's ski!

Me llamo Nitesh. Me encanta jugar al críquet con mis amigos y mi familia.

I'm Nitesh and I love playing cricket with my friends and family.

Whoooosh!

Thwaaacc c c ckk!

Let's bowl!

 Mexico

 UK

 Nigeria

 Switzerland

 Dubai

 China

 Australia

 India

 Spain

 America

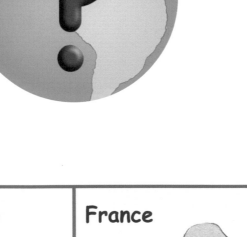 France